monday
morning®

HANDS-ON LETTERS

Puzzle Pals

by Marilynn G. Barr

Publisher: Roberta Suid
Production: Little Acorn & Associates, Inc.

PUZZLE PALS
Entire contents copyright © 2004
by Monday Morning Books, Inc.

For a complete catalog, write to the address below:
Monday Morning Books, Inc.
PO Box 1134
Inverness, CA 94937

Call our toll-free number: 1-800-255-6049
E-mail us at: MMBooks@aol.com
Visit our Web site:
http://www.mondaymorningbooks.com

Monday Morning is a registered trademark of
Monday Morning Books, Inc.

ISBN 1-57612-195-X

Printed in the United States of America
9 8 7 6

Contents

Introduction

Puzzle Pals includes an alphabet puzzle board and puzzle pieces for each letter of the alphabet and a variety of project ideas for creative skills practice fun. Up to four sets of two-part puzzle pieces are designed for self-checking. Upper- and lower-case letters are included. Children will learn to recognize and match alphabet pictures and letters and develop sorting and fine motor skills. Additional Puzzle Pals activities can be found on pages 62-63.

Prepare a workstation stocked with Puzzle Pal patterns and a variety of craft materials for lots of creative skills practice fun. Use baskets or plastic see-through containers to organize the workstation. Store small items in separate plastic resealable bags. Use the Puzzle Pals Supplies Checklist on page 6 to take inventory of supplies on-hand and needed supplies. Reproduce the Request For Craft Supplies form on page 64 for children to take home asking parents to help stock your Puzzle Pals alphabet workstation.

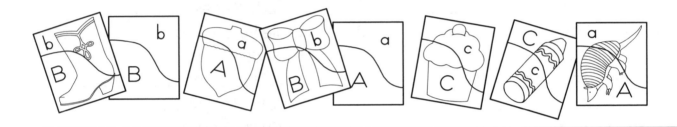

Puzzle Pals

Reproduce oak tag puzzle boards and puzzle pieces for children to make their own Puzzle Pals.

Materials:

Puzzle Pal boards and pieces	scissors	crayons or markers
oak tag	glue	letter-sized envelopes

Reproduce an oak tag puzzle board and puzzle pieces for each child to color and cut out. Help each child cut apart each of their puzzle pieces. Glue a letter-sized envelope to the back of each child's puzzle board to store matching puzzle pieces. Do not glue the envelope flap to the board.

Have each child place all of his or her puzzle pieces, face-up, on a flat surface. Instruct the children to sort, then place one set of matching puzzle pieces on each of their puzzle boards. (Puzzle pieces are designed for self checking.)

Children may place one set of matching puzzle pieces on each of their puzzle boards at a time. Or, they may stack matching sets on top of each other.

Poster-sized Puzzle Pals

Make poster-sized Puzzle Pals to display in an alphabet skills practice center.

Materials:

Puzzle Pal boards and pieces
scissors
glue
yarn
poster board
crayons or markers
hole punch

Enlarge and reproduce puzzle boards and puzzle pieces (pp. 7-58). Color, cut out, and glue a puzzle board onto a sheet of poster board. Color and cut out matching puzzle pieces. Glue one set of matching puzzle pieces onto each puzzle board and the remaining three sets around the poster board.

My Alphabet Puzzle Pals Portfolio

Provide children with materials to make portfolios to store and carry their Puzzle Pals.

Materials:

heavy construction paper
yarn
scissors
crayons or markers
Puzzle Pal boards and pieces
resealable plastic bag
hole punch
oak tag

Provide each child with a large sheet of heavy construction paper. Have children fold construction paper to form a portfolio (diagram A). Encourage children to use crayons or markers to decorate the outside of their portfolios. Help each child punch two holes along the top of his or her portfolio (diagram B). Measure, cut, and tie a length of yarn through each set of holes to form portfolio handles.

Reproduce an oak tag Puzzle Pals board and matching puzzle pieces for each child to color and cut out. Provide resealable plastic bags for children to store each of their Puzzle boards and matching puzzle pieces.

Puzzle Pal Folders

Make and store Puzzle Pals Folders in an alphabet skills practice center.

Materials:

Puzzle Pal boards and pieces	scissors
crayons or markers	file folders
glitter	glue
construction paper	
letter-sized envelopes	

Decorate and write a matching upper- and lower-case letter on the front of a file folder. Reproduce, color, and cut out a Puzzle Pals board. Glue the puzzle board to the inside right-hand panel and a letter-sized envelope to the inside left-hand panel of the folder. (Do not glue the envelope flap to the folder.) Reproduce, color, cut apart, and laminate the matching puzzle pieces. Store the puzzle pieces inside the envelope.

Puzzle Pals Supplies Checklist

Puzzle Pals	crayons	craft sticks
yarn	markers	sand
ribbon	glitter	seashells
twine	glitter pens	pipe cleaners
letter-sized envelopes	wiggle eyes	paper clips
hole punches	cut-out alphabet letters	paint
scissors	sticky dots	paintbrushes
buttons	construction paper	_____
pom poms	cotton balls	_____
manila envelopes	sequins	_____
file folders	beads	_____
star stickers	cotton swabs	_____

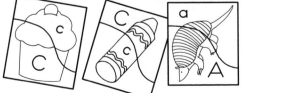

Alligator Puzzle Board

A Puzzle Pieces

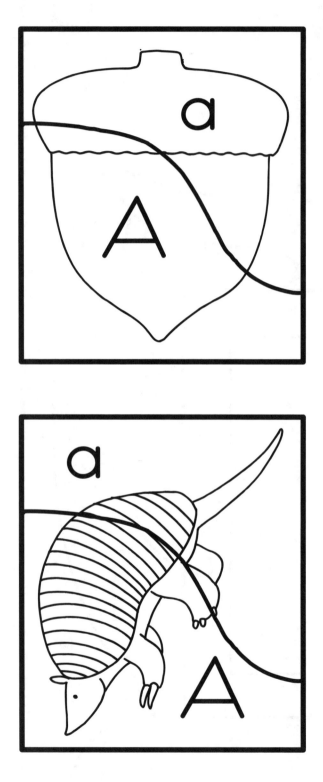

Bear Puzzle Board

B Puzzle Pieces

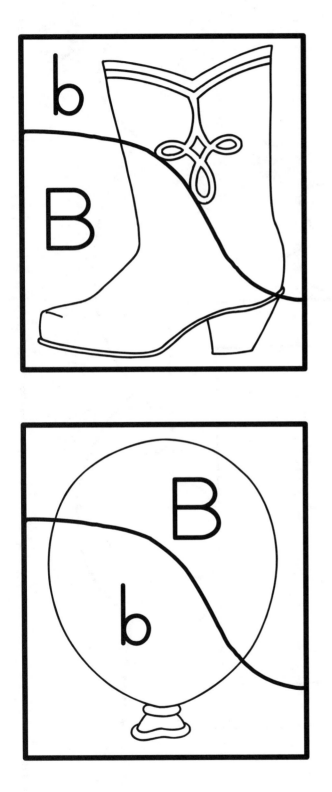

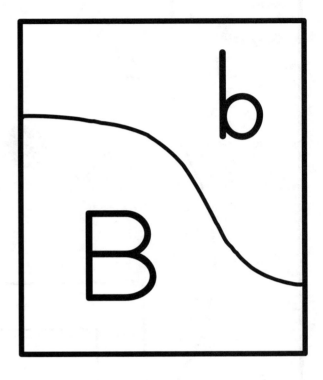

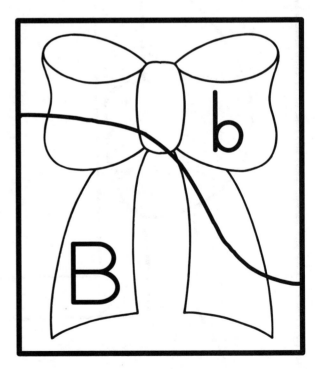

Cat Puzzle Board

C Puzzle Pieces

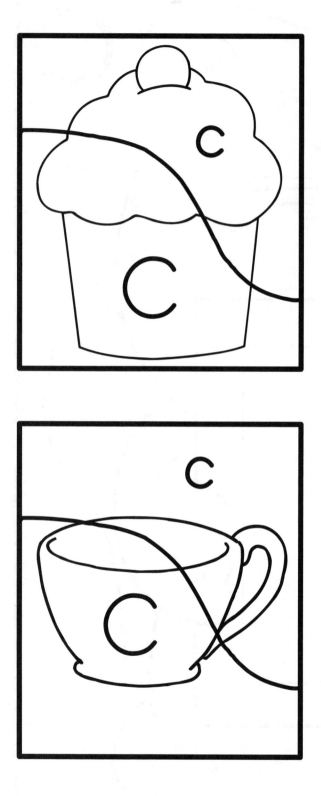

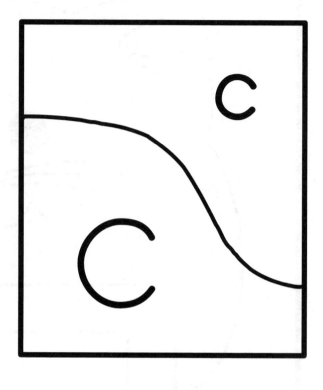

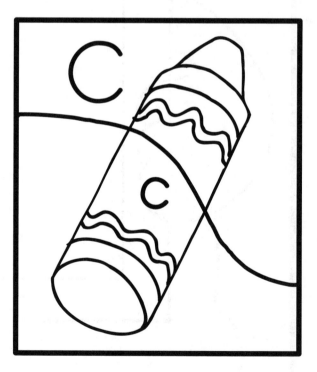

Dog Puzzle Board

D Puzzle Pieces

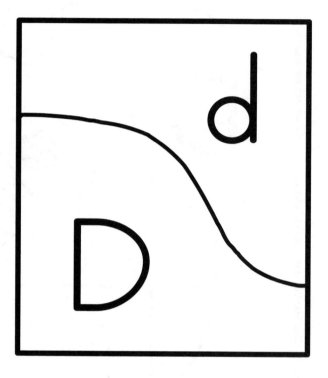

Elephant Puzzle Board

E Puzzle Pieces

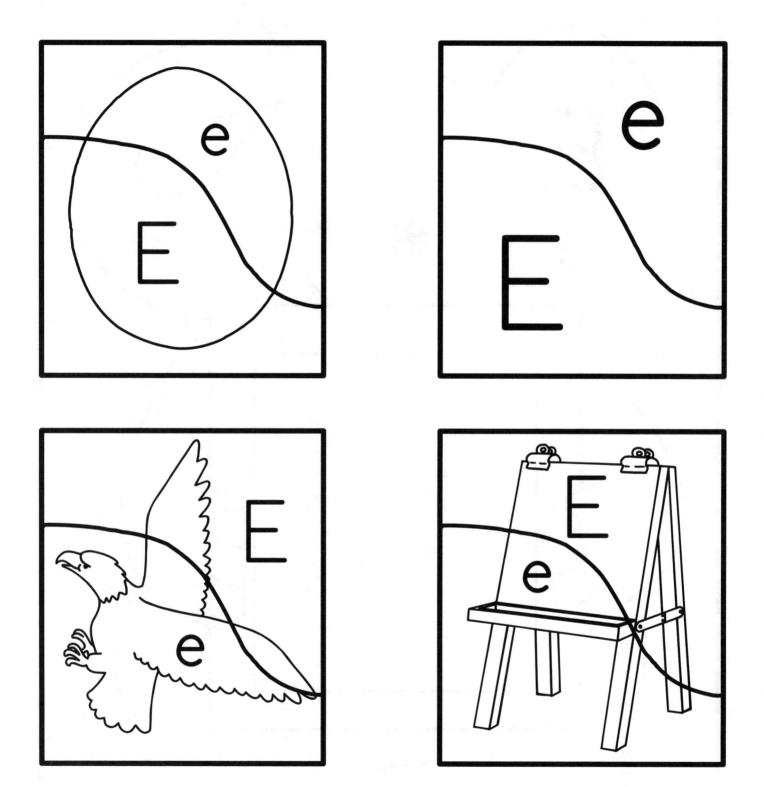

Fish Puzzle Board

F Puzzle Pieces

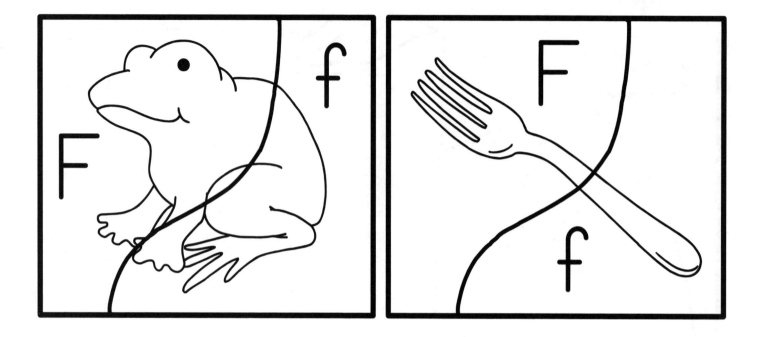

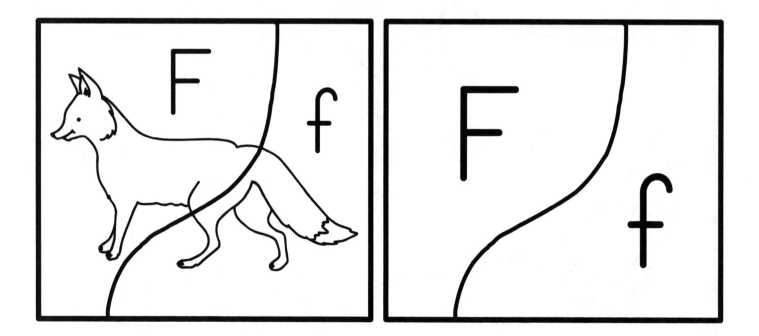

Gorilla Puzzle Board

G Puzzle Pieces

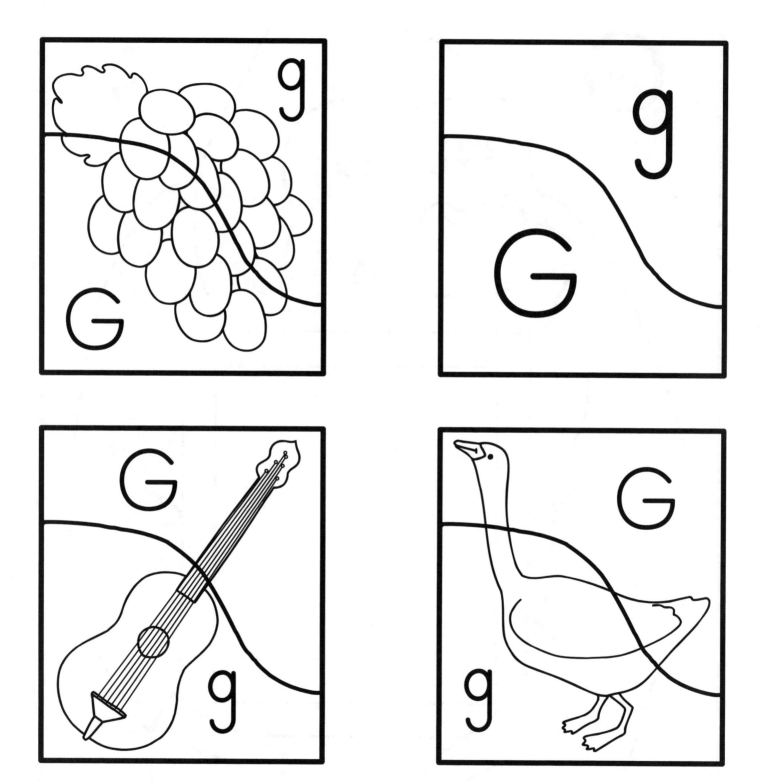

Hippopotamus Puzzle Board

H Puzzle Pieces

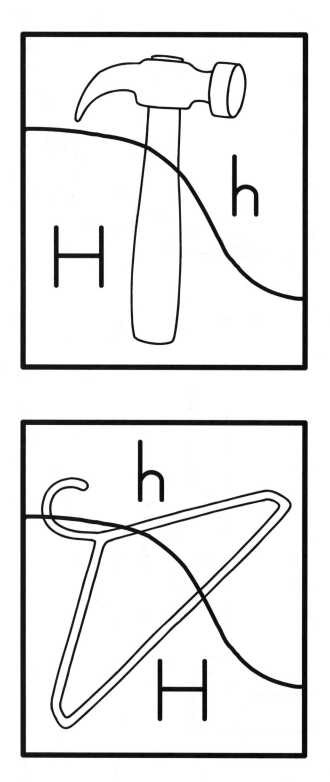

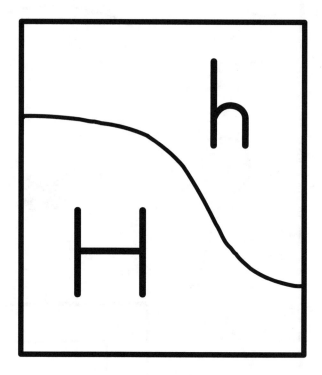

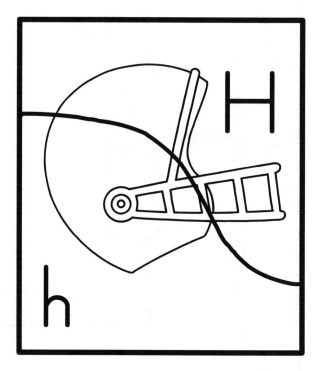

Iguana Puzzle Board

I i

I Puzzle Pieces

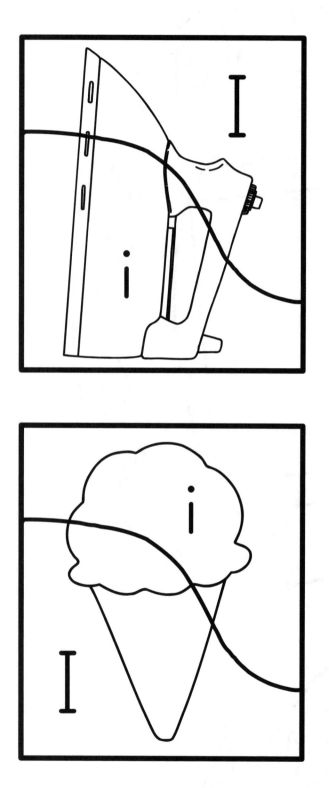

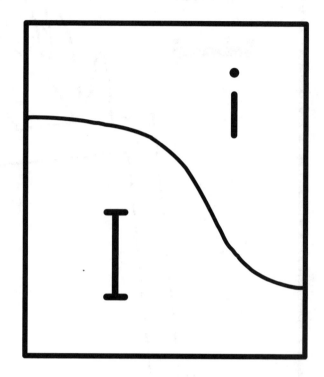

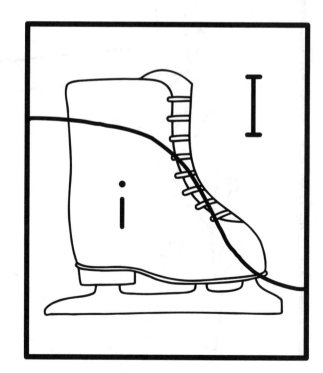

Jack-in-the-box Puzzle Board

J j

J Puzzle Pieces

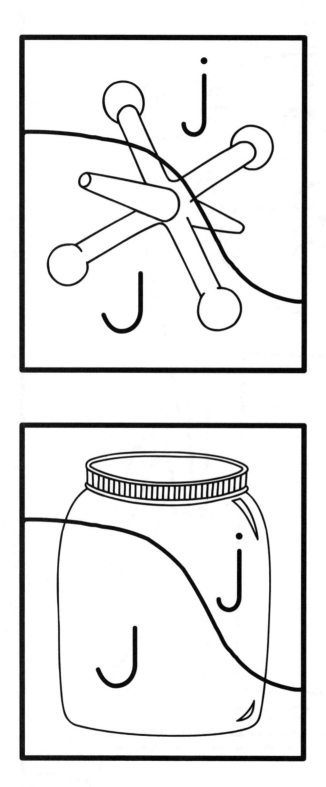

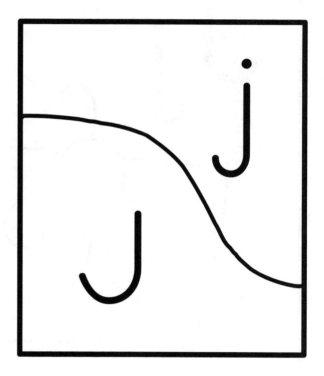

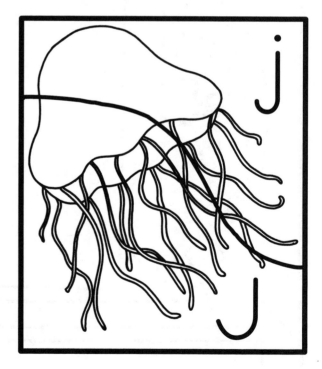

Koala Puzzle Board

K Puzzle Pieces

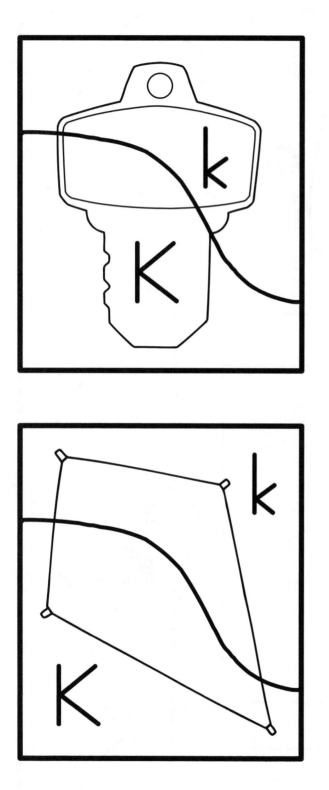

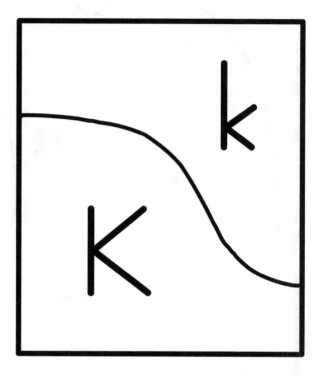

Lion Puzzle Board

L Puzzle Pieces

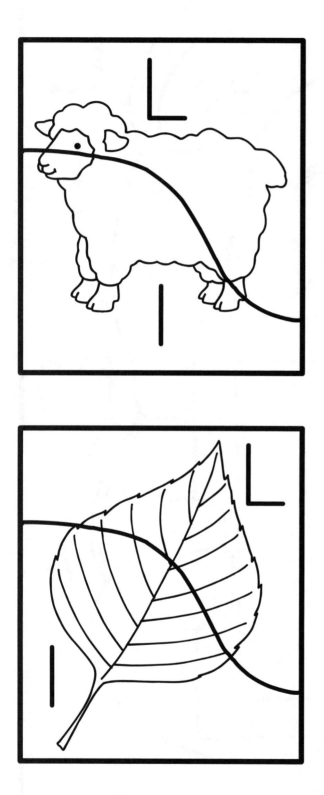

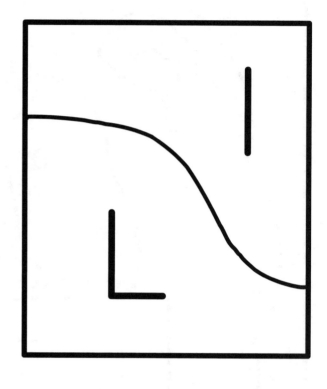

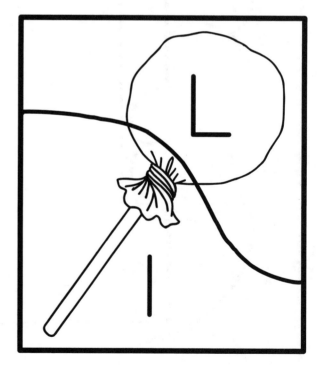

Mouse Puzzle Board

M Puzzle Pieces

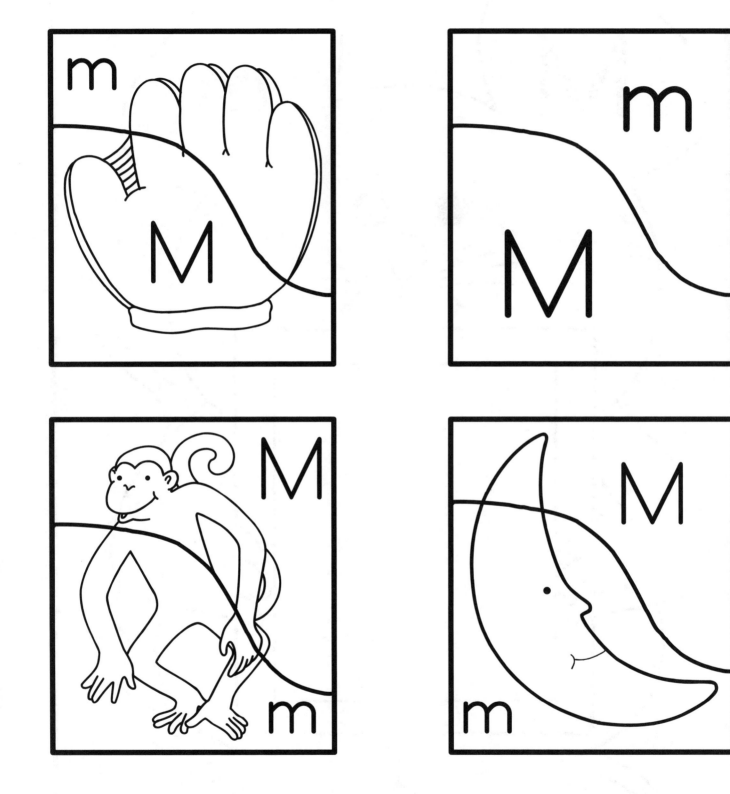

Narwhal Puzzle Board

N Puzzle Pieces

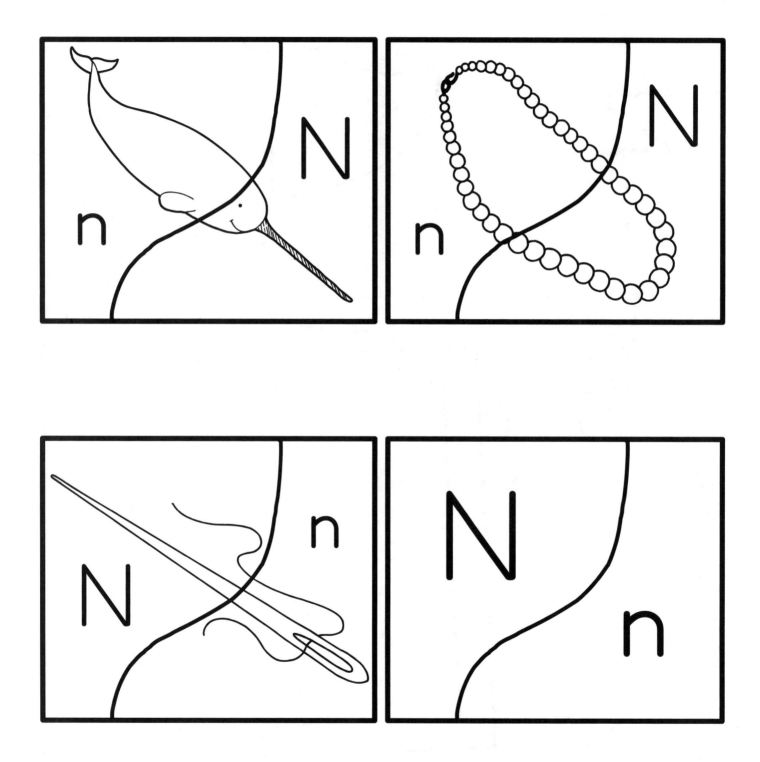

Owl Puzzle Board

O Puzzle Pieces

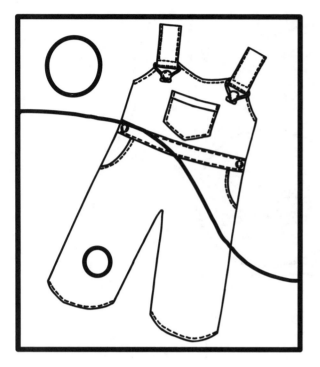

Pig Puzzle Board

P

p

P Puzzle Pieces

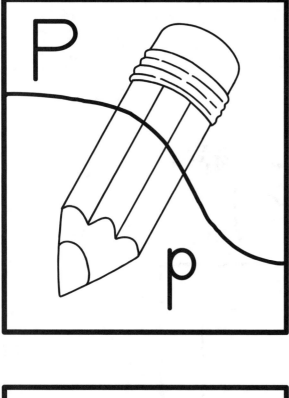

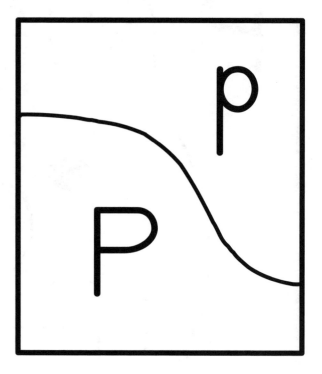

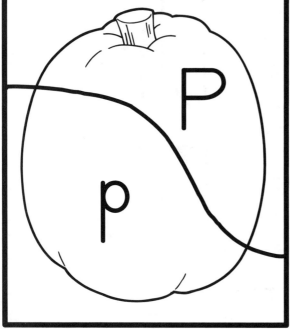

Quail Puzzle Board

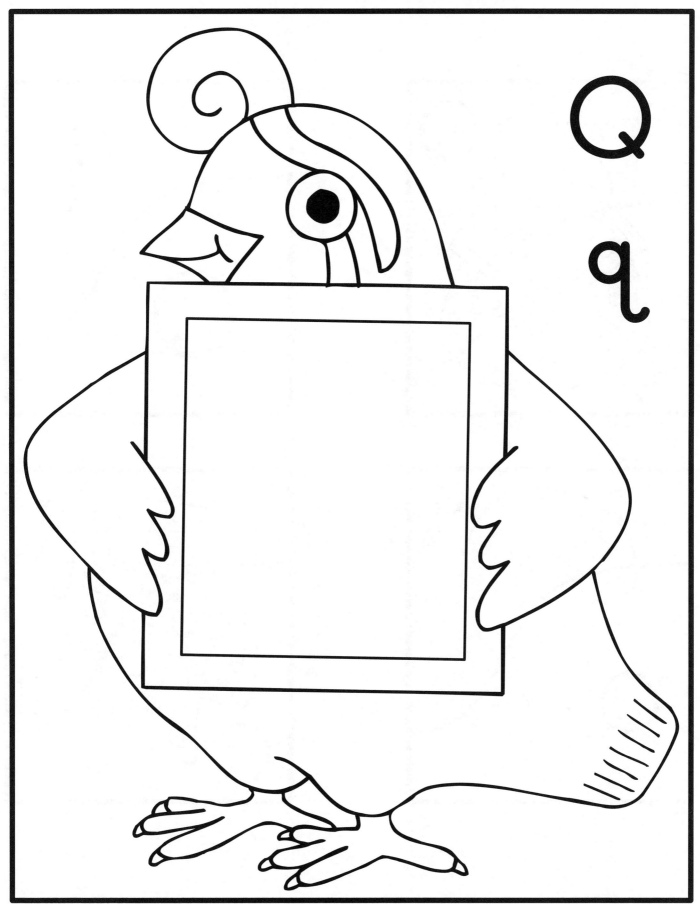

Q Puzzle Pieces

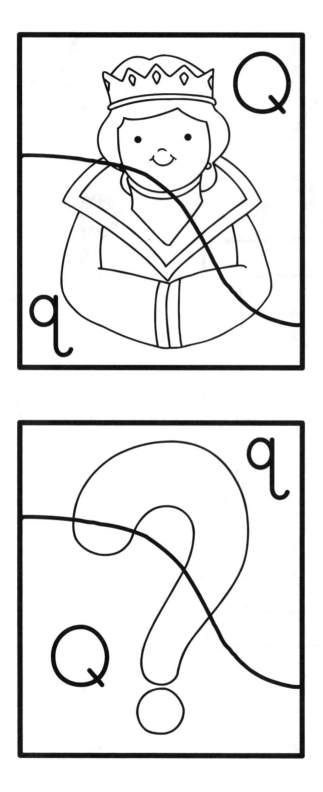

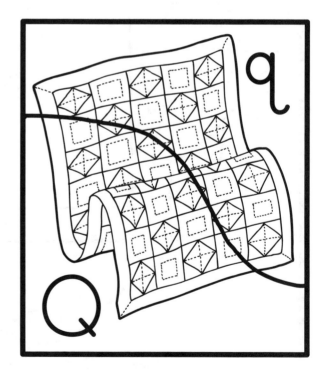

Rabbit Puzzle Board

R Puzzle Pieces

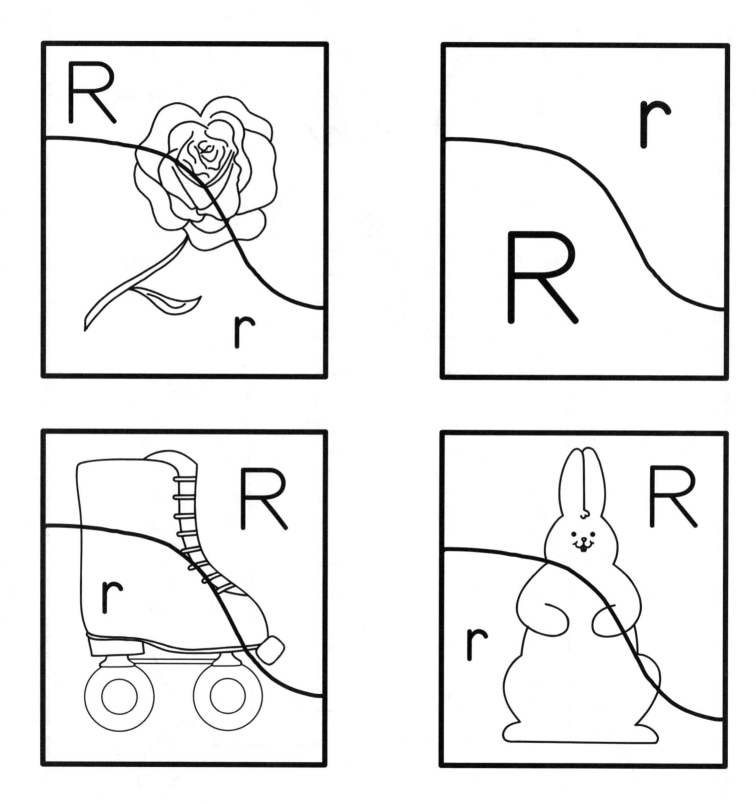

Spider Puzzle Board

S Puzzle Pieces

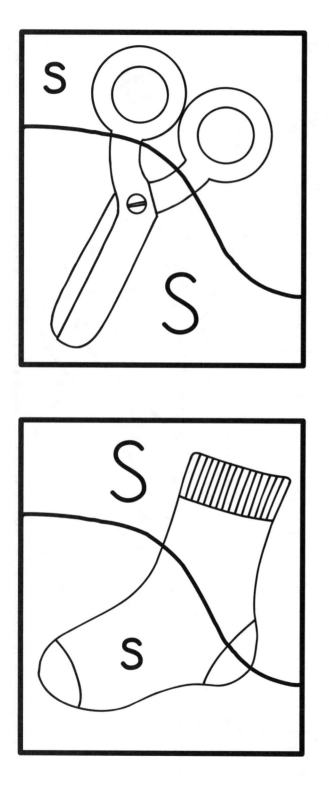

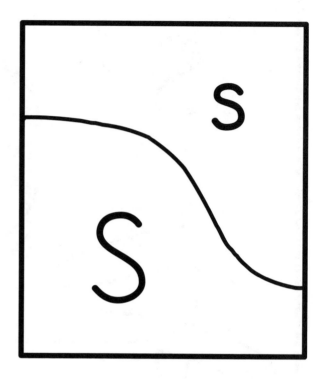

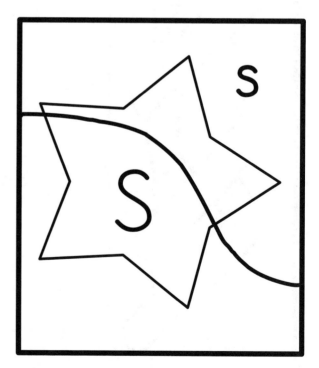

Turtle Puzzle Board

T Puzzle Pieces

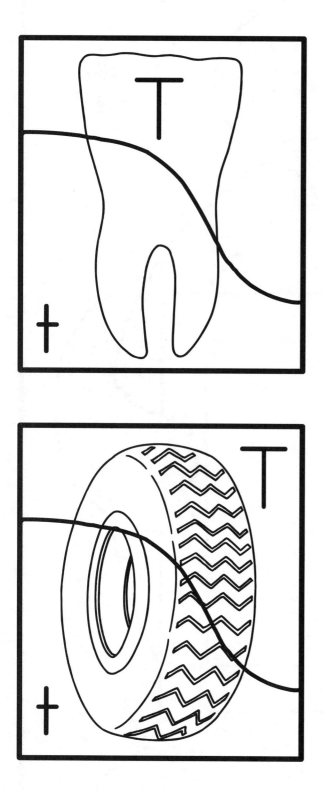

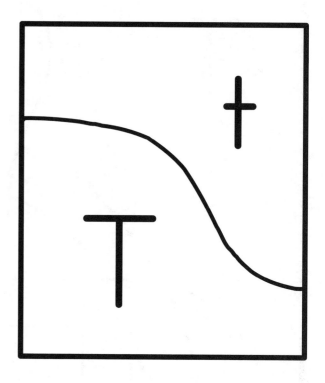

Unicorn Puzzle Board

U u

U Puzzle Pieces

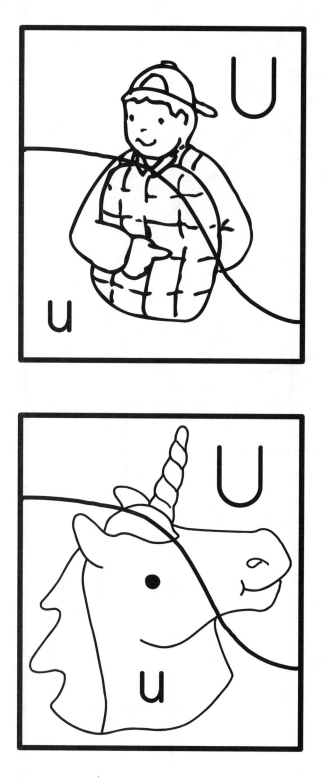

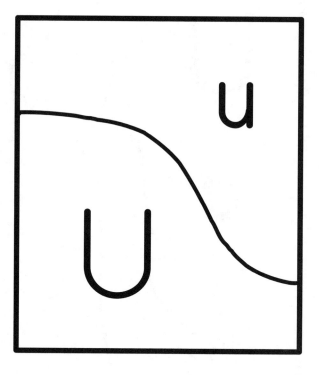

Vulture Puzzle Board

V Puzzle Pieces

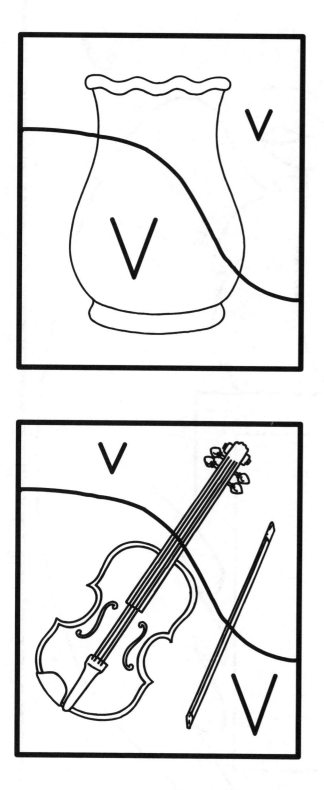

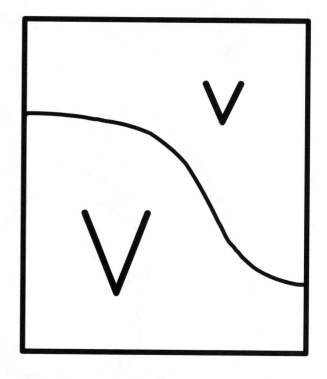

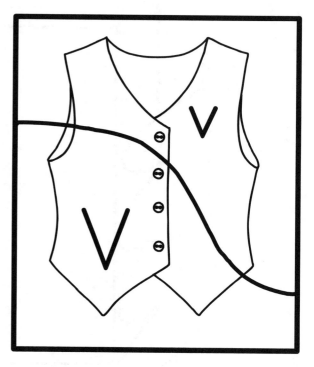

Whale Puzzle Board

W Puzzle Pieces

Mr. X Puzzle Board

X Puzzle Pieces

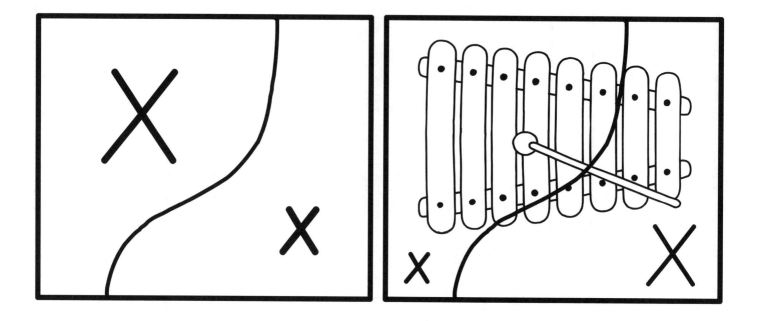

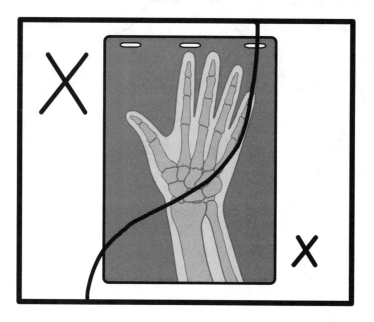

Yak Puzzle Board

Y Puzzle Pieces

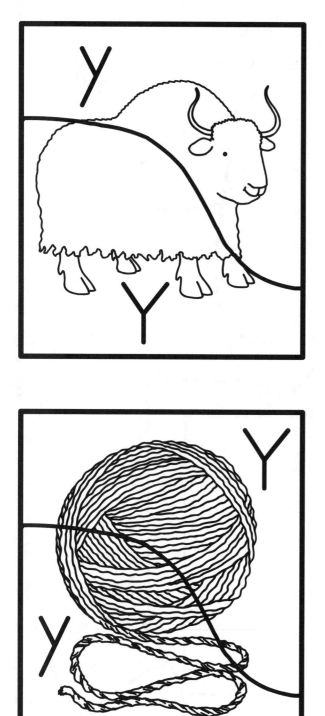

Zebra Puzzle Board

Z Puzzle Pieces

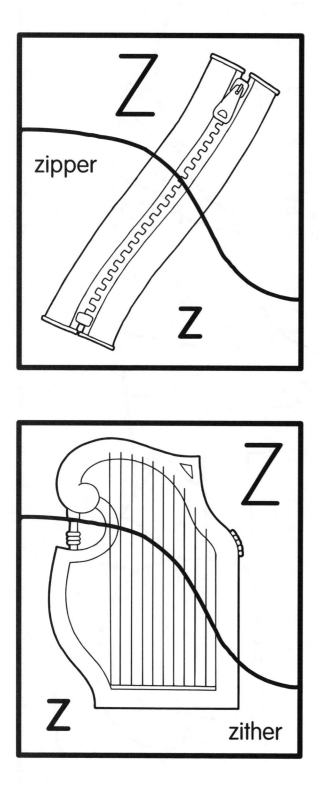

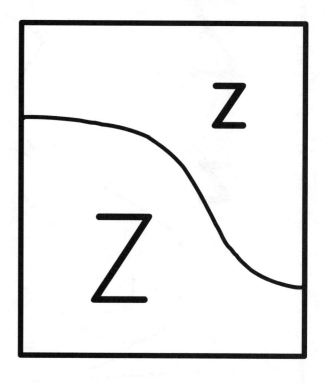

Alphabet Puzzle Board

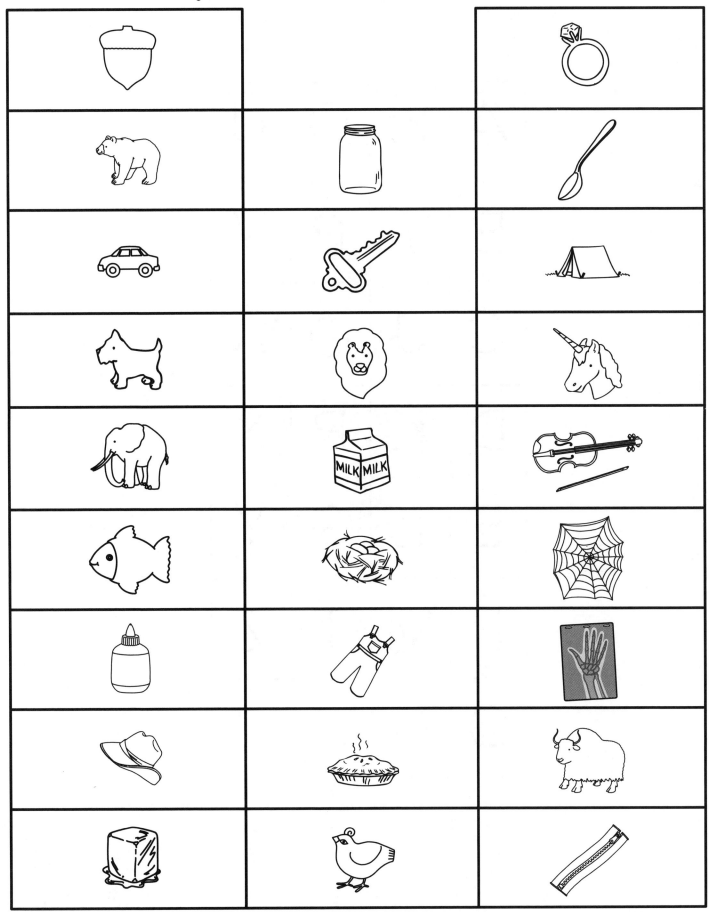

Upper-case Puzzle Pieces

Lower-case Puzzle Pieces

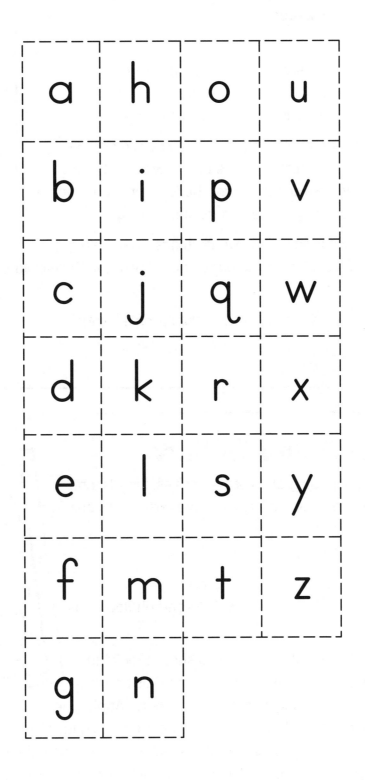

Our Favorite Things Puzzle Pals

Prepare a workstation with a variety of craft materials (see page 6) for children to decorate puzzle boards.

Materials:

Puzzle Pals boards	scissors	crayons or markers
oak tag	glue	glitter
pom poms	buttons	sequins

Reproduce and provide each child with an oak tag puzzle board to color and cut out. (Instruct them to leave the puzzle window blank.) Encourage children to add glitter, pom poms, buttons, or sequins to each of their puzzle boards. Glue decorated puzzle boards onto oak tag.

Engage children in a discussion about favorite things. Then help each child draw a picture of his or her favorite things in the puzzle board window. Write children's names on the back of puzzle boards.

Display finished pictures on a display entitled *Our Favorite Things*.

Puzzle Pals Photo Gallery

Children enjoy looking at photographs of themselves, friends, and family members. Create a photo gallery using the Puzzle Pals puzzle boards as picture frames.

Materials:

Puzzle Pals boards	oak tag	scissors
crayons or markers	glue	wallet-sized photographs
double-sided tape		

Each child will need a Puzzle Pals board and a sheet of oak tag. Have children color and cut out each of their Puzzle Pals boards. Help each child cut out the rectangle on his or her board. Apply glue along the top edge of the Puzzle Pals board, then position and attach it to the oak tag sheet. Lift the puzzle board frame, position, and attach a photograph to the oak tag frame base using double-sided tape. Drop the puzzle frame and secure the bottom with double-sided tape.

Mount finished pictures on a display board.

Puzzle Pals Quilt

Puzzle Pals quilts make colorful displays and are perfect for alphabet skills practice fun.

Materials:

Puzzle Pals boards and pieces	scissors	crayons or markers
hole punch	yarn	glue
heavy construction paper	tape	letter-sized envelopes

Reproduce and provide each child with a puzzle board and matching puzzle pieces. Have children color, cut out, and glue puzzle boards onto construction paper squares. Laminate each quilt square. Tape the bottom and sides of an envelope to the back of each child's quilt square. Do not tape the flap. Have children color the matching puzzle pieces. Laminate, then help each child cut apart his or her puzzle pieces. Store puzzle pieces inside the envelope pockets

Punch an even number of holes along all four sides of each quilt square. Use yarn to lace squares together to form one or more Puzzle Pals Quilts. Hang quilts from cup hooks attached to the bottom of window sills or display boards.

Alphabet Letter Match

Make an alphabet puzzle board (pp. 59-61) for children to practice matching upper- and lower-case letters.

Materials:

puzzle board patterns	scissors	file folder
crayons or markers	glue	tape
magazines and newspapers		

Reproduce, color, cut out, and glue the alphabet puzzle board (p. 59) to the inside of a file folder. Decorate the front of the folder with cut-out letters from magazines and newspapers. Tape a small manila envelope to the back of the folder to store letter cards. Reproduce construction paper letter cards, laminate, then cut apart.

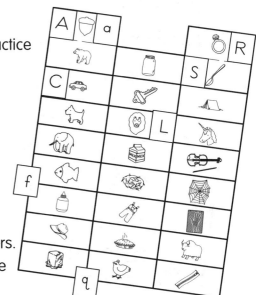

Up to four children can practice matching letters. Place letter cards in a basket. Each child, in turn, draws and places a letter card on the matching alphabet picture space on the board. Play continues until all the cards are placed on the board.

Request For Craft Supplies

Dear Parent,

Please send supplies listed below to school with your child for our alphabet practice workstation.

☐ yarn	☐ star stickers	☐ beads
☐ ribbon	☐ crayons	☐ cotton swabs
☐ twine	☐ markers	☐ craft sticks
☐ letter-sized envelopes	☐ glitter	☐ sand
☐ hole punches	☐ glitter pens	☐ seashells
☐ scissors	☐ wiggle eyes	☐ pipe cleaners
☐ buttons	☐ cut-out alphabet letters	☐ paper clips
☐ pom poms	☐ sticky dots	☐ paint
☐ manila envelopes	☐ construction paper	☐ paintbrushes
☐ file folders	☐ cotton balls	☐ double-sided tape
	☐ sequins	

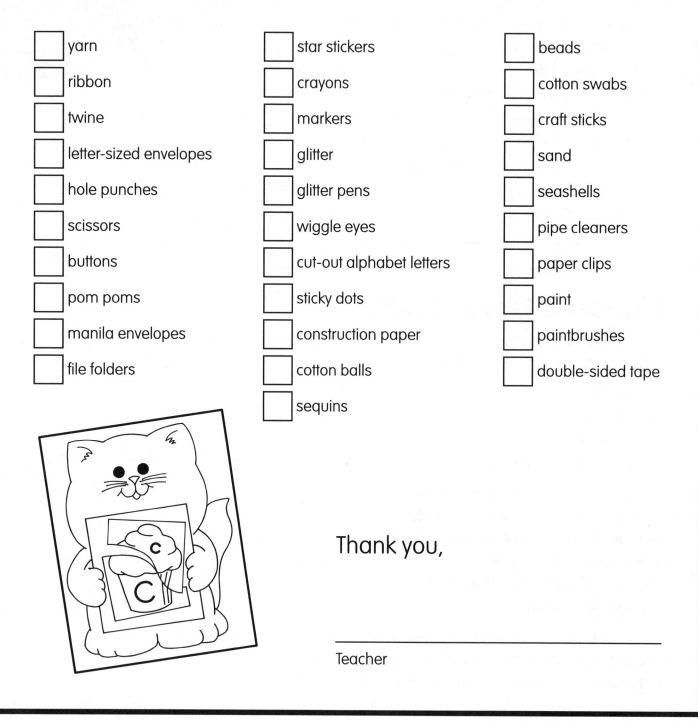

Thank you,

_____

Teacher